MEMORY PALACE

Åbäke

Peter Bil'ak

Alexis Deacon

Oded Ezer

Francesco Franchi

Isabel Greenberg

Hansje van Halem

Jim Kay

Johnny Kelly

Erik Kessels

Na Kim

Stuart Kolakovic

Frank Laws

Le Gun

Luke Pearson

Stefanie Posavec

Némo Tral

Henning Wagenbreth

Mario Wagner

Sam Winston

Hari Kunzru

MEMORY PALACE

Curated by
Laurie Britton Newell
and *Ligaya Salazar*

V&A Publishing

CONTENTS

Every great work of art starts somewhere. That spark, that moment, that instant where the idea takes hold, and grows – that is what excites us here at Sky Arts, to invest in those moments and inspire people on air, online and on the ground. This is why we launched the Sky Arts Ignition Series, where we collaborate with leading arts organizations and artists to create brand-new works, as well as offering five bursaries a year to young artists who are just starting out.

Memory Palace is the second project in the Sky Arts Ignition Series. It's a transcendental story – one of beauty, truth and relevance – and we're absolutely delighted to be working with Hari Kunzru, the artists and the V&A to support the exhibition and bring it to more people across the UK and Ireland.

We hope that *Memory Palace* ignites your creativity, as it has ours.

James Hunt
Director, Sky Arts

Ignition Series

This printed edition of *Memory Palace* by Hari Kunzru appears
alongside illustrations by 20 graphic designers and illustrators.
These concept sketches are the first ideas for the visual
commissions in the *Memory Palace* exhibition at the
Victoria and Albert Museum, London.

Here is how to remember. First you must choose a place. It should be somewhere you know very well. Most people pick somewhere spacious and grand – a great hall, one of the ruined towers of the city. You get to know this place as well as you can. You walk around it, impressing every detail on your memory, until you can tour it in your mind when you are not there. Then you place the things you need to remember around the building, in the form of pictures. These pictures must be startling enough to trigger your imagination. They can be the faces of people you know, or common things combined or altered in an unusual way. A man with the head of a fox. A waterfall flowing uphill. If there is a list of facts you need to remember, you can put them in some specific order. In this way, when you need to recall something, you merely go in your imagination to the spot where you have stored it. There it will be, waiting for you.

When I learned the art of memory, I was living in an old palace in Great Poor Land Street. Before the Withering it had been a library, every room filled with pewter and sign. I knew each corner of that house without having to make an effort, so it was easy to use it to remember by. Later, after I was arrested and confined in this cell, I was afraid I would go mad, so small was it, so featureless and dark. I cried in the night. When I slept I dreamed I was being crushed. So I began to move my memories, to place them round the cell, in the cracks of the floor, on the rusty handle of the slop bucket. By rights, such a small room could not serve the purpose. But I gave each spot a meaning, and as I populated it with the things I have been given to remember, the cell began to grow. It was like pushing the walls outwards with my hands. Now it has expanded to the horizon. To me, it is as grand as a power station.

The Ancient Greeks created an elaborate memory system, based on a <u>technique of impressing 'places' and 'images' on the mind</u>[1]. It has usually been classed as 'mnemotechnics', which in modern times seems a rather unimportant branch of human activity.
In the ages before printing a trained memory was vitally important; and the manipulation of images in memory must always to some extent involve the psyche as a whole. Moreover an art which uses contemporary architecture for *its memory places and contemporary imagery for its images will have its classical like the other arts. Inherited and recorded by Romans, this art of memory passed into the European tradition, to be revived in occult form at the Renaissance, and in particular by the strange and remarkable genius <u>Giordano Bruno</u>. Aside from its intrinsic fascination, the Art of Memory is an invaluable contribution to aesthetics and psychology, and to the history of philosophy, science and literature[1].*

[1] Frances A. Yates, *The Art of Memory*, 1966

Initial references

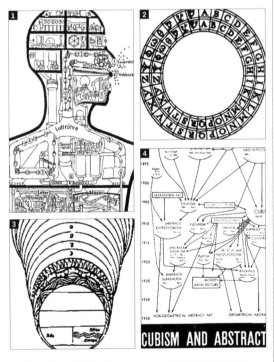

1__Fritz Kahn. Illustration from an explanatory supplement
   to the "Man as Industrial Palace" poster, 1926
2__Memory Wheels. From G. Bruno, *De umbris idearum*, 1582
3__The Spheres of the Universe as a Memory System.
   From J. Publicus, *Oratoriae artis epitome*, 1482
4__Alfred H. Barr, Jr. Cover of the exhibition catalogue
   Cubism and Abstract Art, 1936

Initial bibliography

Frances A. Yates, *Giordano Bruno and the Hermetic Tradition*, 1964

Frances A. Yates, *The Art of Memory*, 1966

Jonathan D. Spence, *The Memory Palace of Matteo Ricci*, 1985

Mary Carruthers, *The Book of Memory: A Study of Memory in Medieval Culture*, 1990

Giordano Bruno, ed. M. Gabriele, *Corpus iconographicum. Le incisioni nelle opere a stampa*, 2001

Uta von Debschitz, Thilo von Debschitz, *Fritz Kahn: Man Machine Maschine Mensch*, 2009

Giordano Bruno, ed. M. Matteoli, R. Sturlese, N. Tirinnanzi, *Giordano Bruno Opere mnemotecniche*, 2009

Daniel Rosenberg, Anthony Grafton, *Cartographies of Time: A History of the Timeline*, 2010

Joshua Foer, *Moonwalking with Einstein: The Art and Science of Remembering Everything*, 2011

Theodore W. Pietsch, *Trees of Life: A Visual History of Evolution*, 2012

Initial sketches / vertical solution

Diagrams of the memory systems and links....................

History of art of memory....................
<u>Timeline</u>: from Frances A. Yates, *The Art of Memory*, 1966

1700 The art of memory and the growth of scientific method....................

1620 The theatre memory system of <u>Robert Fludd</u>....................

1590 <u>Giordano Bruno</u>....................

1580 <u>Lullism</u> as an art of memory....................

1570 <u>Ramism</u> as an art of memory....................

1550 Renaissance memory <u>Giulio Camillo</u>....................

1450 The art of memory
400 in the Middle Ages....................

50 BC The three Latin <u>sources for the classical art of memory</u>....................

500 BC The art of memory in Greece....................

The method of *loci*....................

<u>Sources:</u>
A- *Ad Herennium*
B- *De oratore*, <u>Cicero</u>
C- *Institutio oratoria*, <u>Quintilian</u>

<u>Artwork proportions:</u>
$\frac{h}{W} = \phi$ *(Sectio Aurea)*

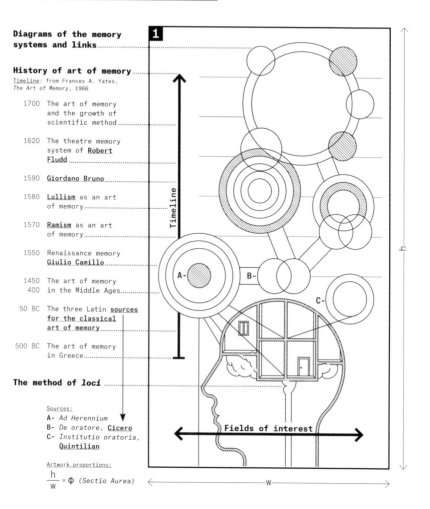

Initial sketches / alternative horizontal solution

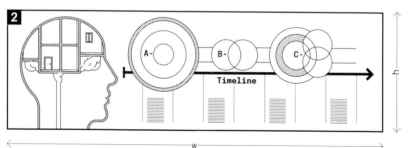

*

I have been charged with membership of an internet. There has been no trial, just a meeting of thanes in the Great Hall of the London Thing. Though they use these words – *charged, internet* – they don't really know what they mean any more. They are words from before the Withering.

They use the words out of vanity, mostly. The men who gathered to question me have no more notion of information-age Laws than they do of *physics*, or *evilution*. But they are terribly insecure and terribly righteous. They are to be the bringers of the Wilding, the ones who will make the world anew. They are the swaggering lords of the red and the white and the green.

Ignorance is only purity tarnished by scorn. That is the slogan. Knowing nothing should be cherished: it's a sign that you're free of trace. Secretly they are not sure, these great lords. They have doubts, alone in their chambers at night; they feel the chill hand of death tapping on their shoulder. So when they puff out their chests and bring down their thunder on the likes of me, they cloak it in old-time words, because those words have power.

Such thunder as they can muster.

In their bones, the Lords of the Thing know they are small men, compared to the sign-wielders, the builders of hospitals. However much they exalt themselves, they know. The shadows of the ruined towers fall on them as they walk through the city, just as they do on the rest of us.

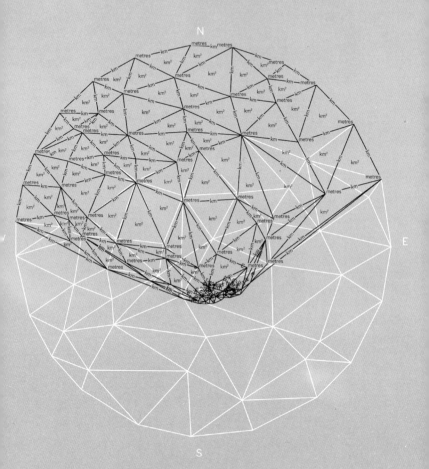

*

People have different visions of the end, but all agree it is coming.
The Wilding might be a joyful harmonizing with nature. It might feel
like throwing down a heavy burden, straightening upright after being
weighed down by civilization for so many centuries. Or it might just be
nothingness, our exit as a species from the world's stage. Some think
that would be a blessing. They are hastening to bring it about. After
what our ancestors did, we don't deserve to strut around like masters
of the earth. We should be ashamed, hang our heads. Without us
crawling on her back, the great Mother would breathe more freely.

*

I am afraid. To those monsters of ego, the Thing, with their tattoos and
their plaid and their clan signs, the rest of us are just attendants. Each
one thinks he is the hero of the story, that the end of humanity is just
a colourful backdrop to his personal drama of election and sacrifice.
If one of these men wanted to lay my body at his feet to serve him on
his journey to the afterlife, he wouldn't hesitate for a moment.

The Lords of the Thing are possessed by one kind of madness. There
are others. Some want to be overcome, swept away into the Wilding.
They're looking forward to their extinction as a moment of great joy.
It's hard to be an individual, to be conscious and alive inside the prison
walls of your skull. So much easier to lay all that aside, to flow into
something larger than yourself. So much easier to forget.

I am not that kind of person. My eyes are open, I look around. Yes,
there's something larger than me: I live in its ruins. There are very
few of us, in the shell of the teeming city that stood here before the
Withering. We pick about for things we can use. We are stunted,
ravaged by disease. My fellow Londoners, can't you see how we
are diminished? Where is your pride?

*

Here is a story that occupies a niche just above the peephole. From my bed, I can see it as a broken arch, under which stand two boys, holding hands. This story is radiant. It shines out to me like a beacon in the darkness.

> There was a banquet, given by a wealthy man. A poet
> spoke a poem in praise of the host. Only half of this poem
> was about the virtues of the wealthy host, about his
> generosity, his wisdom, the pleasures of his table. The
> other half was about a pair of divine twins, to whom the
> poet was devoted. The host was angry, and sarcastically
> announced that he would only pay the poet half of the
> agreed fee for the performance. He should seek the rest
> from the divine twins, wherever they were to be found.
> A little later, a message was brought to the poet. Two
> young men wanted to see him outside. He rose from
> his seat and went out, but no one was there. Just at
> that moment an earthquake struck, and the roof of the
> banqueting hall caved in, crushing the wealthy host and
> all his guests to death beneath mounds of rubble. The
> corpses were so battered that the relatives who came to
> claim them were unable to tell who was who. But the poet
> remembered the seating plan for the dinner, and was able
> to name each of the dead from the position of the body.
> He was hailed by all as a master of the art of memory.
> The twins, who had called him outside, had repaid
> him handsomely for his praise.

The Thing have all sorts of insulting terms for us. They call us a cult, a corruption, an internet. We call ourselves Memorialists. If nothing else, we are the ones, in this ruined place, who can recite the names of the dead.

*

Once there were great palaces called hospitals. The tradition of
hospitality was revered across the land. It meant helping customers,
healing them and seeing to their needs. Men and women greeted each
other by asking 'How can I help you today?' The doctors performed
great feats of surgery and roamed the cities, looking for the sick, whose
faces would appear on their screens so that all men would know who
was in need.

It was a time of great wonder.

*

At the winter festival we burn effigies of the great Lawlords, in their white coats. Most people don't know their names any more, just that they were terrible villains and were punished by the Magnetization.

I know the names of all seventy-two Lawlords, along with their attributes and their colours and their primary Laws. They sit in a row on the rivets that line the metal door of my cell. Among the greatest was Milord Rayleigh, who knew why the sky was blue. He made great Laws for the sunset and the sound of distant bird calls. There was Milord and Lady Ayn Stein, who wrote the Laws of Relativity and The Invisible Hand, and Lords Ferryday and Pastor and Lady Mary of the Cure. Lord Ferryday carries two glowing orbs. Lord Stein holds out a trader's screen, brimming with sign.

On the bars of the window, I have placed the three great Laws of Milord Newton, on which all the prosperity and glory of the ancient world rested. These words are known by all of our sect. They are the first thing we memorize. When they are taught, there are always two Master Memorialists present, so that the sins of error and variance will not creep into our remembering.

Tower of London

interior

heraldry

Vanadium

parliament

Big Ben

St pauls

Victoria Palace

Law I

*Every body persists in its state of being at rest or of
moving uniformly straight forward, except in so far as
it is compelled to change its state by force impressed.*

Law II

*The alteration of motion is ever proportional to the motive
force impress'd; and is made in the direction of the right line
in which that force is impress'd.*

Law III

*To every action there is always an equal and opposite
reaction: or the forces of two bodies on each other are
always equal and are directed in opposite directions.*

In this Law is hidden the secret. In this secret is our beginning. Out of
the action and the reaction come knowledge of metal and the hidden
paths of stars. The Thing have made it a capital crime to speak aloud
the words of Newton and the other Lawlords. If you speak and they
come to know you have uttered a Law, they will call you a whitecoat
and make you suffer torments. Your guts will be drawn on rods. You
will be pierced and branded. Your eyes will be put out and your tongue
plucked at the root.

*

My cell is – just a cell. To anyone else, it must appear almost featureless. The walls are bare plaster, peeling in places to reveal patches of grey brick. There is a metal door with a peephole and a hatch low down near the ground, through which food and water can be passed. There is a metal-framed cot and a thin mattress, wrapped in some kind of hard-to-tear fabric. Pushed against a little wooden table, so that it stands no more than a foot from the side of the bed, is an armless wooden chair.

I have been here a long time. Months, certainly. I'm not sure any more. I am adrift in time and space.

On the floor next to the door, just at the foot of the bed where I don't have to look at it all the time, is a slop bucket, flecked with rust on its handle and base. The floor itself is lined with white tiles, a few of which are broken, leaving dark gaps like missing teeth. High up on the wall opposite the door is my only source of light, a small recessed window, which lets in a weak yellowish glow. The window glass is thick and grimy. It is blocked by two vertical iron bars, cemented into the recess.

B)

The table, the bed, the rivets in the metal door – nothing about this cell is specific. None of it carries a trace. I could be anywhere, at any time in history; there have always been places like this. One thing I know: the blankness is not an accident. It is the meaning of my cell, the message my captors want to convey to me.

A long time ago, the walls must have been painted a drab green. Then this colour was painted over with an equally drab grey. Little bands of these two colours remain in the window recess, a wider band of grey and a narrow, barely perceptible strip of green, framing the square of yellow light.

*

Old London was really three cities – the City of Waste Monster, the City of Dogs and the City Itself. On a tile just by the head of my bed, I have placed a list of the ancient gates. It looks like a gold ring, with gems set into it, each a different kind of stone.

The names of the gates are

Moregate	The Edge Where	Bankers Mount
Farringdown	Bays Water	The Temple
Bard's Beacon	Notting Hell	The Mansion
Kings Curse	High Keen and South Keen Singtown	Cangate
Use Town		Mourning Mount
	Slow Square	
Great Poor Land Street	Victor	Tower Hill
Baker Street	Waste Monster	Liverpoor Street

Their gems are

	carnelian		malachite	
obsidian				sapphire
	zircon	agate	moonstone	
diamond				quartz
	aquamarine	chrysoprase	jade	
onyx				garnet
	opal	emerald	ruby	
beryl				amber
	topaz		amethyst	

The names of the gates were taught to me by Osmon Jason, who was killed by the grey wolves of the Thing eight years ago. He had it from his father Osmon Kirk, who had it from a man called Phelps Aleph who is said to have owned three thousand books. Phelps Aleph, who wrote sign and wielded electricity as if it were water running through a pipe.

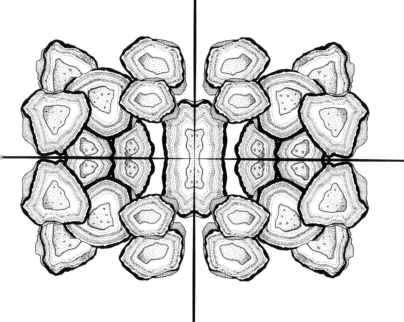

*

In the time before the Withering, there was a religious practice called *Recycling*. It was a ceremony to celebrate the cycle of life and the turning of the seasons, just as we light torches and nail the green man to the cross at the winter solstice. Men and women would chant: *I am not a plastic bag*. They would reduce by fasting and going on photoshop. As they trod the stepper (a kind of dance) they would venerate the old things of the past year, adding them to the vast treasuries which were known as *landfills* because they were filled with all the good things of the land.

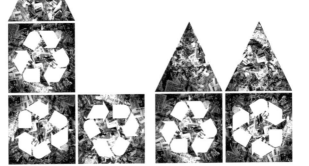

*

The time before the Withering is known as the *Blooming* or *Booming*.
In the Booming there was a rage for accounting. They accounted the
sand on the riverbank, the number of breaths they took as they flew from
city to city in their schools, flights so long that children would grow older
in the air, graduating from economy class to business to first or master
and even doctor degree. Accounting is how the great doctors learned to
build sign. It set up the towers and hospitals and razed them again with
bombs. At the height of the Booming, sign was so plentiful that it fell
from the sky like rain. It rustled underfoot in autumn and rose
and fluttered about the palaces and hospitals like apple
blossom in spring. This was called *advertising*.

*

When I was first seized by the wolf bands and brought here, I was beaten, then left alone for several days. The only water was in the slop pail. On the third day I was hooded and walked up many flights of stairs. When the hood was taken off, the light was so bright that I couldn't open my eyes. All I could see was a figure, a silhouette, and the light streaming in behind it. To me, so used to cowering in darkness, he seemed like a Lawlord, a god.

Little by little, my eyes grew accustomed to the light. The room was very plain, with whitewashed plaster walls and bare boards on the floor. I was standing – or rather cringing – in front of a polished wooden table, behind which a man sat in a high-backed chair. Behind him was an open window, through which summer sunlight was streaming. I saw that we were very high up. Beyond the window was nothing, just the blue sky.

The open window, the light, the fresh air. I felt ashamed of myself. My clothes were smeared with dirt and excrement. I was a creature from a lower world, out of place in such a room.

My interrogator was dressed in a heavy kilt and a homespun shirt. On his broad, flat-nosed face were tattoos of rank. Everything about his person was clean and neat: his cropped hair, the single bone ring on his finger. He looked at me without showing any particular sign of disgust.

THE THIRD DAY

When he asked me my name, I said nothing. He asked again.
His voice was low and gentle, like a woman's. It sounded too soft,
too – *civilized* for a thane, a high official of the Thing.

Again I did not answer. Then he surprised me.

'What is this terrible enthusiasm you have for ideas?'

'What?' My voice came out as a croak, a papery rasp.

I should not have answered. But he didn't speak how those men
usually speak. We are all taught in the moots and gatherings that
a man expresses himself simply and uses humble words. He does
not simper. He does not try and leave a trace in the air. But this
man says *enthusiasm, terrible enthusiasm*. Such an ancient phrase!
Words to drink in like wine.

I heard the question coming out of my blistered mouth. I'd already lost;
right then, with that first ploy, he had me in his grasp.

'Ideas,' he said, 'are not things. They are what you have
instead of things. Instead of the good solid wood of this
table. Instead of the water I know you crave.'

And he took a jug and poured out a beaker of water, began to drink.
I watched him drink his fill. I watched beads of moisture run down
the beaker. I could feel the breeze on my face. I tried to concentrate
on that, the little whisper of good clean air on my face.

'Ideas,' he said, 'don't quench your thirst. You may think
they give you power, but that's a lie. How can an idea
have power over matter? They are completely different
in kind.'

He waited, as if I would give him some answer. But I was already
growing wary of this man, who talked, not like a solid thane, but
like one of us.

He fixed me for a moment with his eyes and frowned, pulling the
blue bar inked over his brow into the shape of a bow.

'And of course ideas are a poor substitute for true power.
True power lives in the bone. It courses through the
blood. Even you should be able to see that. We are men.
We were meant to be warriors. We were meant to exist
in a wild world.'

He poured out another glass of water and left it sitting on the table as
he got up and started to pace the room. I knew I made a wretched sight.
My hands were bound behind my back. I was so weak from thirst and
hunger that I could barely stand up.

'A wild world,' he said into my ear. Quietly, in his
incongruous woman's voice. 'This is what we're working
for. We're trying to find our way back to the feeling of the
wind on our faces, the taste of cool fresh spring water
in our mouths.'

And he raised the cup to my lips. I gulped down water and it ran over
my chin and soaked my filthy shirt and it was the most blessed drink
I ever had.

Then he must have given a command, because men came and took
me back down to my cell.

*

These words are banned. *Minute, second, meet* and *centimeet, centigrade* and *fair-in-height. Inch, gram* and *mile.* Any *kill-oh* word. Any *terror* or *gigger* word. Any *mega* or *minimum* or *mole* or *molecule* or *milly* or *minicule* or *bite.* There was once an *international system* of accounting. It was this *international system* that collapsed, causing the world to wither. From this we know that the roots of the old world were steeped in number. When the sap of numbers dried up, the towers drooped and the screens went grey and crumbled to dust.

The *system* had a palace in the city of New York. This was its headquarters. Its hindquarters were in Africa, perhaps in the old cities of Lagos or Kenyatta. It united all the *nations* (a name for men loyal to the same brand) and regulated every kind of accounting, imposing unities called *standards*, which fixed the whole world in time and space. The Thing hates accounting more than any other crime. The punishments for it are terrible to behold.

Why are they so afraid? I have made an *equation*, which is a word for a bundle of sign with no body. Here is my *equation*:

> *Accounting is the opposite of Wilding. The more men*
> *account the world, the less wild it will be.*

I wish I could write this as it should be written, with the equals and the plus and the squared root. But I cannot write. The last true writer died ten generations ago. I wish I could even speak my equation truly, speak it in numbers and coax from it the living sign. This was one of the great powers of accounting, the power of number to cleanse the people of error and variancy. But I have no powerful numbers, just the common ones, the one and the two and the three and so on, who release no energy when split. I have more knowledge of number than most, it's true. These days, the phrase 'forty' is used to mean 'very many'. If you have a band of forty men, you are a great lord.

*

Customer
One who is treated according to the ancient customs.

Internet
A conspiracy of fools and knaves, a plot against nature.

Photoshop
A ritual conducted before going out into the world, in which the face and stomach are anointed with a powder called *picksels*.

*

Before they brought me to the Lord Inquisitor a second time, they
sluiced me down and gave me a set of new clothes. They were rags,
a buttonless shirt and a pair of baggy trews that I had to hold up with
one hand. In the white room, the broad-faced man sat at his table.
He told the guards to unbind my wrists, and had me lean forward
and hold out my hands, palms facing upwards. I thought then
that he would put me to the question, and braced myself for pain.
Instead, he took my hands in his.

> 'Feel my palms,' he commanded, looking me directly in
> the eye. His gaze had neither pity nor malice; he looked
> at me the way you would at a tree or a stone. 'I am proud
> of these calluses. They do me honour.'

Then he twisted my wrists and examined my palms.

> 'You've done work too. That's something. What kind?'

'I was a farmer. I worked at a farm camp.'

> He shook his head. 'Soon enough we'll have done with
> all that. If I had my way, we would never have started.
> Farming is work, of a sort. But still – dragging a plough
> across our Mother's back, opening her up to fling in a
> few seeds? It's demeaning.'

'I was ordered to work there. None of us were free men.'

    'It was regrettable. Those places don't bring us
    any closer to the Wilding.'

'What, do the men of the Thing not need to eat?'

Suddenly he brought his fist crashing down on the table.

    'That is not how a man eats! Alien things coaxed out
    of the ground! Bow your head! Don't look at me!'

I did as I was told.

    'You dare question me? A man hunts. This is how
    nature ordained it in the beginning, before we trod
    the Sorrowful Road of civilization.'

I said nothing, and looked at the floor.

    'You know the steps of the Sorrowful Road?'

'Yes, sir.'

    'Speak them for me.'

'The first step leads to the farm gate, the second to the marketplace. The third leads to the factory. The fourth leads to the tower. The fifth leads to the library. The sixth leads to the bunker and the seventh to the pewter room.'

> 'Very good. And what happens if the warrior opens
> the farm gate and steps inside?'

'He shall stoop and bend his neck.'

> 'Exactly. So do not lecture me. I am a warrior.
> I have never stooped. I have never bent my neck.'

'No, sir.'

> 'But you? You have taken many steps along
> the Sorrowful Road. You are far along.'

All I could think was *lecture*? That was a banned word. No thane would utter such a word.

*

There was the time of Booming. Then the great moral evil of the
Lawlords brought the Magnetization. It was not a thing, as some
people believe. It was not a plague or a war. I had this from a Master
of our fellowship who had it from his own Master, who was old enough
to have fought on the steps of the London Library. It was a vision.
An electrical vision.

An aura was seen all over the world, great waves of light shivering in
the sky. They saw the great waves of light, and their screens spewed
out their last sign and went dark. After that, all memory was gone, and
the market was empty and the people wandered the cities looting and
burning and killing one another. It is said that the people had lived in
the realm of sign so long that no one could remember how to get food,
and without pewter they no longer knew their own names and could not
prove to each other that they were kin. Husbands did not know their
wives. Mothers did not know their children. It was a war of all against
all, each against each.

*

The third time I was brought
before the Lord Inquisitor,
he had on his desk the proof
of my crime. It was a piece of
sign, a pattern of marks joined
together like a frame.

Inside the frame were
intricate signs:

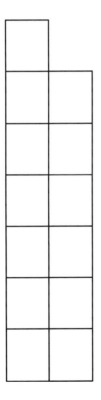

H	
Na	Be
K	Mg
Rd	Ca
Cs	Sr
I	Ba
Fr	Ra

It was part of something sacred and mysterious, called the Great Table of Elements. In the ancient libraries and hospitals the alphabet marks were chanted as a prayer:

```
/       x x              x   /
Hey-na bee!           Rod-car
/       x x            /  /  /
Kay-em-gee!           Shri Ba Fra!
```

This prayer is sounded in the language of *science* or *signs* or *signscrit*, which is the ancient language of the Lawlords from the time of the Booming. I don't know how to read the marks. I was taught how to make them, but I was never supposed to set them down. They were meant to be in my memorial, as indeed they are, sitting along a crack in the floor under my bed. I was supposed to keep them until we could use them again.

But I liked to look at them, at the landscapes of loops and lines. They made me think of hills and stormy seas and fire brimming out of molten rock. So I set them down. It was reckless; when I was taken by the wolves, they found the paper. It was trace, than which there is no greater crime. The Wilding will bring the end of trace. It will be the end of all signs separated from bodies. The bodies will just be, without sign to fly over them. All the things of the world inside themselves, dumb and silent, unnamed: that is the Wilding.

There is a slogan:

Language is a snare.

The Thing want to cut us free from the trap of words. They say we are caught and need to get away.

hydrogen										
1										
H										
1.0026										
lithium	beryllium									
3	4									
Li	Be									
6.941	9.0122									
sodium	magnesium									
11	12									
Na	Mg									
22.990	24.305									
potassium	Calcium	scandium	titanium	vanadium						
19	20	21	22	23	24					
K	Ca	Sc	Ti	V	Cr	Mn	Rh	Fe	Ir	
39.098	40.078	44.956	47.867	50.942	51.996					
rubidium	strontium	yttrium	zirconium	niobium	molybdenum					
37	38	39	40	41	42		Ru			
Rb	Sr	Y	Zr	Nb	Mo					
85.468	87.62	88.906	91.224	92.906	95.94	Tc				
caesium	barium	lutetium	hafnium	tantalum	tungsten					
55	56	71	72	73	74					
Cs	Ba	Lu	Hf	Ta	W		Re			
132.91	137.33	174.97	178.49	180.95	183.84			Co	Os	
francium	radium	lawrencium	rutherfordium	dubnium	seaborgium			Hs		
87	89	103	104	105	106		Bh			
Fr	Ra	La	Rf	Db	Sg				Mt	
[223]	[226]	[262]	[261]	[262]	[266]					

helium
2
He
4.0026

carbon 6 C 12.011	nitrogen 7 N 14.007	oxygen 8 O 15.999	fluorine 9 F 18.998	neon 10 Ne 20.180
silicon 14 Si	phosphorus 15 P 30.974	sulphur 16 S 32.066	chlorine 17 Cl 35.453	argon 18 Ar 39.948
gallium 31 Ga	germanium 32 Ge 72.61	arsenic 33 As 74.922	selenium 34 Se 78.96	bromine 35 Br 79.904	krypton 36 Kr 83.80
indium 49 In	tin 50 Sn 118.71	antimony 51 Sb 121.76	tellurium 52 Te 127.60	iodine 53 I 126.90	xenon 54 Xe 131.29
thallium 81 Tl	lead 82 Pb 207.2	bismuth 83 Bi 208.98	polonium 84 Po [209]	astatine 85 At [210]	radon 86 Rn [222]

B Al Ga
Cu Pd Zn Ni Cd
Au Ag Hg
Uun Uuu Pt
Uub Uuu
Au

*

Museum

A palace where the Lawlords went to muse. Museums were
filled with treasures kept for musing on or *amusement*.
These palaces were silent and heavily guarded, because
even in the Booming, amusement was precious and rare.

The Inquisitor steepled his hands.

'What are we to do with you?'

'You will do whatever pleases you, I expect, my lord.'

He pointed to the leaf of sign. 'You know what this is?'

I shook my head.

'I think you do.'

I looked at the ground. 'My lord, I'm just a poor pedlar ...'

His rage was sudden, blazing. 'Do not think you can play with me! Do not make that mistake! You will tell me where you got this! You will tell me who gave it to you! And then you will tell me what foul tricknology you hoped to cast with it!'

It was then they put me to the question. I will not describe what they did. It is something I would rather not remember.

*

I remember the light of the sun between storms, when the air was clear and carried no scent of waste or burning.

I remember a wiry-haired little dog which I kept as a pet. He would roll on his back and lift one leg in the air, quivering, begging to have his tummy rubbed. He was a sweet-natured, cowardly little dog.

I remember the driving rain and the mud. I remember the ache in my back after a day working in the fields.

These are my memories. They belong to me. I don't see why they must disappear into the Wilding.

I was born in the Campers, a holding about five days' walk from the city. It was a cluster of ancient palaces, set on a heathland, high boxy halls once bright with windows, now just skeletons patched up and weatherproofed with scavenged wreckage. When I was small, I found magic in the place, the way the earth around the halls glittered with diamonds of shattered glass, the tiny scraps of sign that lay about, caught under rubble, silted up in forgotten corners. I had a few keys from a qwerty, and even wore them as a kind of charm, tied round my neck with a leather thong. I think my da must have hung them on me, for luck or protection. No one bothered about bans or edicts; the prohibitions on sign meant little back then. The Thing and London were just names to us. I grew up believing the world ended at the top of Far Field.

-THE CAMPERS-

— THE ISLE OF SHARD —

THE LIMPICKS —

Like all the people of that place, my family was in thrall to a thane who styled himself Vice Chancer, after the great lords who used to rule there in the Booming. We grazed his stock and gathered his corn and sang songs to him at the harvest festival as he sat at High Table with his posse. When I was a small child, the Chancer was an old man with a white beard and watery pale blue eyes, but after he died, the holding was inherited by his son, whose gaze was fierce and fixed on his goal – to build himself a great storehouse of wealth and sit on top of it with his dogs and his wives and his iron axe and never come down.

We were just hands to this new thane, there to be worked until we dropped. Hands to hold shovels, to heft stones out of the way of the plough. Times got so hard that when I was about ten years old we packed our things and ran away. On a moonless night my da led us up on to the heath, my ma, my two brothers and me, all laden down with heavy bags of food and clothes. For a while we lived on the road, hiding from the Vice Chancer's men, who had been sent to fetch us back, but my father was clever and had friends, and so we evaded them and came at last to the brick wastes of the London suburbs and then to a great city slum known as the Limpicks, where I was to spend my years until manhood.

My first sight of the Limpicks was terrifying. The skyline was dominated by the giant metal figure of the Red Man, his twisted limbless torso rising up against the sky, every strut festooned with strings and rags and prayer flags, fixed there by the pilgrims who came in their thousands, all hoping to be released from suffering, to go into the Wilding without more pain. Below him was a warren of narrow streets lined with cramped shacks, clustered around the great cracked oval of the ancient arena. The Limpicks was a midden, a foul-smelling hive. Waste clogged the open sewers. Lean, evil-looking dogs scavenged through the rubbish. The old river had flooded almost up to the edge of the site, which was built on a kind of cliff of trash that slid down into a treacherous marsh, teeming with snakes and fevers. It was a place to get lost in, which is what my family did.

We set up as pedlars, selling trinkets and flags to the pilgrims. I got
used to the swirl of stamping feet, the chanting and wailing. I used to
love coins, the worn silver heads of the ancient lords and ladies. It was,
I later found out, one of the last places they were used. Coins were one
of the reasons the Thing had their eye on the Limpicks. They didn't like
trade – as everyone knows, the marketplace is the second step on the
Sorrowful Road. They didn't like the cult of the Red Man, because it
looked back to the Booming, and was not under their control. To them
the Limpickers and the pilgrims were a potential source of rebellion.

Soon I grew used to the rhythm of the place. Every morning, people
crowded on the edge of the cliff to void their bowels, drawing buckets
of marsh water to sluice themselves down. Sometimes there were
corpses in the water, of people or animals, but no one paid them any
mind. I would squat, one of a line of jostling arses, scrub myself with
a brush and then pick up my tray and go to fight my way through the
crowds at the Red Man's feet. If I had money, I would eat a pasty or a
rice ball. If I had none, I would go hungry until I had sold something.

I got used to the pilgrims, to their hungry eyes and their pleas to the
twisted metal god to solve their problems. I never got used to the
flagellants, who thumped their chests and scourged themselves with
spiked flails until their backs had the look of ground meat. They felt
the Withering was born of their sin, and looked to the Red Man to
punish them, to beat them down into unknowing. Some crawled rings
round the giant figure, prostrating themselves at each step. Others
slithered their way like worms.

Occasionally someone would set himself on fire, a circle of fascinated
pilgrims gathering to watch him jerk and twitch in his mantle of flames.

When I was about seventeen, the Thing made a proclamation
outlawing the cult of the Red Man. The herald sent to speak it was
surrounded by guards, nervously holding their pikes out towards the
crowd. The Red Man, said the herald, in his high quavering voice, was
a relic of the bad old world, and his worshippers a foul internet whose

only purpose was to rip good people away from their roots in the earth. The Limpickers should immediately give up their heresy and affirm their fealty to the Thing. We responded with knives and rocks, and the herald ended the day dancing at the end of a rope, surrounded by a baying crowd. The Thing's revenge was swift and brutal. They sent in riders, who fired the shacks and rounded up as many of us as they could find. I only escaped by hiding in the marshes, sunk up to my eyes in the stinking water. The riders forced their captives into a kind of pen at the Red Man's base, and piled up trash and scavengings all around it, before setting it ablaze. I lay in the marsh until nightfall, shivering with cold and listening to the screams of the dying.

My ma, my da and my two little brothers were in that cage.

I heard that the next day the Thing attached cables to the Red Man and tried to pull it down. They dug out the base and attacked it with saws and hammers. But it was too large for them to move it, too firmly planted in the ground. I say I heard, because I'd already fled, heading further into the old city with no more than the clothes on my back.

I don't remember much about that time. My mind was clouded with grief and hatred. I know that later I settled in Great Poor Land Street, not far from the site of the Old Library, where the readers had made their last stand in the early days of the Withering. It was then I met Billgee, who would be my teacher.

Billgee was only one of his names. At times he also asked us to call him Tewring or Ferryday – all names of Lawlords, banned names which it was death to utter. He had others which he used among non-Memorialists, but these secret names, though they were not his, seemed to lend him power, and in return to take a little power from him, as if by using them he was bringing the Booming a little closer, brightening its light.

Billgee was a tall man, with a diagonal scar across his face from right to left, which seemed to divide it into two sections, old and new. He spoke to me as I was trying to weatherproof my shack against the summer storms, which in London are strong enough to sluice away whole streets. He asked me where I was from, and said he'd heard I was curious about the time before the Withering. These were dangerous words, but for some reason I trusted him. What he said was true. From childhood, I'd always kept my eyes and ears open for anything about the ancient days. Not for any particular reason, just because hearing about them made me happy, made me feel life had a meaning, a purpose. I asked him what he knew of the Boomtime, and he told me he was a *historian*. This was the word he used. It was the first time I'd heard it. He told me if I was to follow him, he'd show me a secret place. I put down my tools and said lead the way.

We climbed over a pile of rubble into one of the old hospitals at Use Town. Hidden in the depths of the building was a door, which led down a steep flight of steps into a tunnel that Billgee said was called a *tube*. People once got inside these tubes and travelled from one place to another, following lines of different colours. We trudged along the tube by the light of a lantern, until we came to a kind of cave, with raised banks on either side. The walls were tiled, and here and there were embedded pieces of coloured sign, the clan colours of old London, the red and the white and the blue. I saw that we had come to a treasure house, filled with tricknology. There were piles of qwerties, ancient screens whose black surfaces had a sort of half-shine, the deep half-shine of captured light, the kind of colour we can't make any more because we've lost the secret. We climbed up on to the banks, and he showed me stacks of boxes, flat and featureless on some sides, indented with complicated holes on others. These, he explained, were pewters. They were filled with number. If we were to breathe power into them, they would spill out the speech of dead men and pictures that moved without a guiding hand. Beside the pewters were belts of plastic, some with carved buckles that, as he showed me, were made to connect the pewters to the power that the ancient Lawlords had coaxed out of the earth.

I hadn't known before how pewters had to be tied into the earth to show and speak. This new learning felt wonderful and yet somehow plain, as if it had always been in my mind. It was a feeling I would have time and again as Billgee told me more about the ancient city. That day, until the lantern began to gutter and we had to turn round and find our way out, he showed me marvels: green boards studded with tiny jewels, dusty piles of bound sheets scored with sign and sometimes even pictures. I'd seen very few pictures in my life, and certainly none like those. They were faint – some barely visible, just dustings of pale blue and yellow on the brittle screens – but they were, I think, the most beautiful things I had ever come upon – impressions of strange and mysterious events, men and women dressed in fabulous costumes, engaged in all the wondrous activities of the Boomtime.

After that I became Billgee's disciple. He taught me many secrets – the powers of the Lawlords, the stories and customs of the old city. He told how the day was once divided into twelve parts called hours, and how those hours were themselves divided and divided again until the smallest blink of an eye had a name. He taught me the operations, the times and the miners and the plus, how to coax one number from another and make them do my bidding. I thought I was Billgee's only pupil. Then one night he asked me if I was ready to make a pledge. I said I was, and he asked if I would risk my life to salvage something from the ruins of the past. Again, I said yes. The future seemed dark and the present was the domain of the Thing. To me, the past was the only source of hope for our blighted world.

Together we walked a winding route through the old city, towards the drowned towers. Billgee seemed nervous, looking behind us to see if we were being followed. At the water's edge, a man was waiting for us with a boat. He rowed us through the towers, towards the great ruin known since ancient times as the Shard. It lay at the edge of the southern marshes, where the old city had been completely drowned by the rising water. Over the generations, refuse had washed against its base, fusing together into a sort of spongy island. As we climbed out of the boat I felt the ground give way slightly beneath my feet.

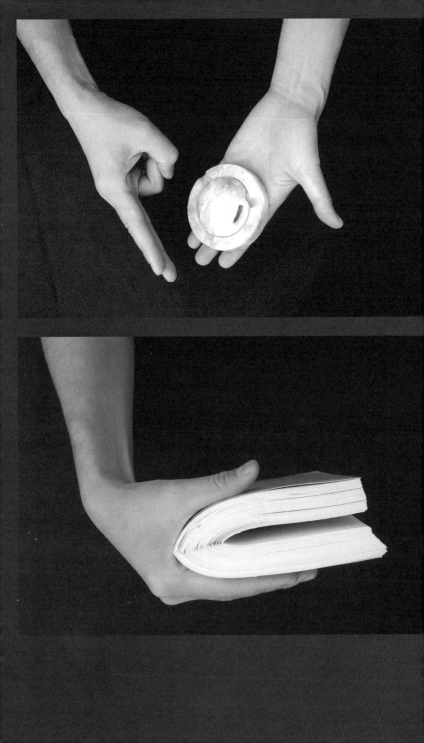

Inside the Shard's shell a silent crowd was waiting for us. Never had I felt more hopeful. So many comrades! So many who refused to go into the darkness without a fight! At that meeting I was inducted into the fellowship of the Memorialists. I swore never to betray the trust placed in me, to strive to bring back the glory of the Boomtime.

The next day I began to study the art of memory. With Billgee's help I'd already assembled a whole mental library of ancient knowledge. Now, for the first time I understood what it meant to be an internet. We shared our learning. It flowed between us like sign, even though none of it was true sign, just our spoken words. To ask questions, hear answers: it was beautiful, heart-filling. I understood why the Thing feared it so much. Our way was to double as much as possible, so if one of us was betrayed or killed, the work would not die with them. We lived in constant fear. The Thing knew of our existence, and used spies and informers against us. To be a Memorialist is to live in the shadow of death. That's something we understand about the world. The darkness is always snapping at our heels.

I was coming along in my learning, and had been trusted to bear some deep memories, when disaster struck. I was walking alone in the Bell Raver, an unfamiliar quarter of the city, when I was taken by a farm gang. It happened suddenly, without warning. I heard footsteps behind me and was hit hard on the head. I fell and that was it for me. When I woke up, I was bound hand and foot, bumping along a road in a cart with twenty other folk. I knew straight off what had happened. I was on my way North.

By then I understood the many differences between the teachings of
the Thing and its actions. They taught that as the Wilding approached,
we would abandon the fields and make gardens in the forest. Soon
we'd abandon even the gardens, because nature, being in balance
at last, would provide us with abundance, without the need to clear
or weed or sow. It would be an eternal harvest. The wild would grow
over us, pouring sweetness into our mouths.

But for the moment nature was not pouring sweetness into our mouths.
The people were starving. In the city we cleared small patches for
vegetables, and raised rodents and rabbits, or hunted them with dogs.
The Thing needed to feed their riders, but since farming was degrading
work, they would not set their men to it. In places like the Campers,
local thanes controlled the farms. Elsewhere, they just used slaves.

For the next three years I was a serf on a farm in the great waste north
of the city. We grew corn and soy and oilseed, but above all we grew
rice. Huge paddies were owned by the High Lords of the Thing, and
thousands of us laboured there. We slept in shacks by the side of the
fetid water, plagued by insects, shaking with fever. When workers died,
the Thing just shipped in more.

I would have died myself, had I not managed to escape. One night
I slipped out of the barracks, with a bag of rice grains scavenged over
weeks and months from the threshing floor. I found my way back to
the city, where I made contact with the fellowship, and was greeted
as one risen from the dead. When I asked after Billgee, I heard he
had disappeared. No one seemed to know if he was alive or dead.
I never had news of him again, and to this day I mourn him as I do
my own parents, burned up in the fire.

*

Who is your teacher? What was your plan? Speak louder.

Just a name. Then it will stop.

*What is this screen? We know you intended to make some
mischief with these signs. What are their powers?*

I can't hear you.

*You are young. You could still have a life. There is no reason to be here.
You should be outside, with the wind on your face.*

*The world is not made of facts. The world is not made of lists of nonsense
from the age of information. It is made of rock and wood and water.*

You have forgotten how to be humble.

*You only need to make a sign for something you have repressed.
What you no longer feel in the blood and in the bone.*

I will have to teach you to be humble.

You will give me a name.

*

After they took me back to my cell, I lay on the floor, watching the pictures in my memory palace spin and turn, gorgeous and bright. For the first time I could see them – not just in my mind's eye, but in reality. They were as real as the slop bucket. They were so very beautiful.

*

Manager
Those who barely got by, who could not live
in a world of such quickness, and starved.

Feedback
The grain that was stored against famine, in giant *silos*.
The alertness of the guards was checked constantly.
These guards were known as *Minutemen*.

Bombing

A bomb or boom was energy in a small space. In the
beginning there was a seed or *paradigm*, which exploded,
growing the towers and the hospitals and the bridges
and pradas and ponzis. They used bombs to feed the
great bubbles that surrounded the cities, protecting
them from the dangers outside the box. The bubbles are
said to have shimmered with such opulence that weak
or downsize men were driven mad.

Voicemail

A kind of armour made of speech, which managers used
to protect themselves from intrusion and assault.

Enterprize

The good things of the earth were distributed to all. There was
such abundance that even the lowliest was showered in riches.
Enterprize was the wealth that came to the people of the Boomtime,
just by virtue of *entering* or being born. From this wealth,
the cleverest and most talented extracted *content* or happiness.
The evil ones who brought about the Withering dissipated
their enterprize in *synergy*, or wasteful lust.

*

For a long time they left me alone. Time passed strangely, in loops and stutters. I couldn't be sure if I was going forward, or living the same moment again and again.

My body was broken, but I had told them no secrets. I had crawled into the cave of myself, too deep for my interrogator to follow. For a long time – days, I think – I lay without moving, curled up in my hiding place, not wanting to come out and face what had happened to my hands, my feet, my teeth, my tongue…

Food was pushed through the hatch in the door, but I didn't eat. I stared at the walls, the floor, the simple furniture of my cell, but I barely saw them, so blinded was I by the beauty of the memory palace I had built. It appeared to me as a huge, all-encompassing tower, shining with all the glory of the past. It held hordes, swarms, armies – all the world I would ever need. I had no wish to leave.

Then they came for me again. I was hooded, hauled upright. My wrists were bound behind my back, my crushed fingers pressed agonizingly together. I thought I was going to the interrogation tower, but instead of the long climb, I was taken down a corridor and out into the open air. They half carried, half dragged me. I couldn't walk without help.

I smelled woodsmoke and dung. I thought I was on my way to the execution ground and tried to make my peace with the world. I said goodbye to my friends, to the places I had known. I prepared to go into the dark.

I was lifted on to a cart, which lurched away. I could hear the horse's hooves, the rhythm faltering as it picked its way over the uneven track. As the journey went on, I realized that we weren't heading towards the gallows at Soon Square, but somewhere else, somewhere open and wild, where flocks of crows were cawing overhead and the wind was whipping at the burlap sack covering my face.

At last the cart stopped and hands lifted me down to the ground.
The hood was removed. Blinking in the light I saw that I had been
brought to a hill overlooking the city, one of the old burial mounds
made at the time of the Withering. An ancient roadway wound its way
towards the drowned towers of the City of Dogs, breaking off suddenly
where its supporting pillars had collapsed. Above us, birds wheeled
and tumbled in the sky, more than I could ever hope to number.
A mega of birds. A milly. I could see far into the distance – the smoke
rising from cooking fires in the slums, the limewashed buildings
of the white quarter, the flat grey expanse of the southern marshes,
broken here and there by islands of debris.

The guards withdrew. Beside me stood my Inquisitor, who looked me
up and down, like a tinker checking the condition of his merchandise.
He seemed happy; his broad flat face was tense with expectation.
He threw his cloak back on his shoulders and began to chant.

'Can the principle of selection, which we have seen is so potent
in the hands of man, apply in nature? Let it be borne in mind
how infinitely complex and close-fitting are the mutual relations
of all organic beings to each other and to their physical conditions
of life. Can it, then, be thought improbable, seeing that variations
useful to man have undoubtedly occurred, that other variations
useful in some way to each being in the great and complex battle
of life, should sometimes occur in the course of thousands of
generations? If such do occur, can we doubt (remembering that
many more individuals are born than can possibly survive)

that individuals having any advantage, however slight,
over others, would have the best chance of surviving and of
procreating their kind? On the other hand, we may feel sure
that any variation in the least degree injurious would be rigidly
destroyed. This preservation of favourable variations and the
rejection of injurious variations, I call Natural Selection.'

As he sang, I was curious, confused, and then struck with a kind
of awe. He was reciting, without error or variancy, the great and
mysterious Law of Milord Darwing, who bred the fantastical plants and
animals of the Booming – animals which have since vanished, plants
which have degenerated into the noxious weeds that choke the fields
in the farm camps. Darwing is hated by the Thing almost as much
as Milord Newton. They say he tore the Mother limb from limb and
crossed men with fish and insects. It was beyond my understanding
that a High Lord of the Thing would know Darwing's words, let alone
be able to recite them from memory. I had them from a Master of our
sect, and this beast of a man, whose tools were the rack and the iron
and the screw, knew them as well – or better – than I did. The words
he used sounded purer, even, than the ones I knew. It was like hearing
the true language of an ancient Master of sign.

'How do you know those words?'

'Does it matter? They are just words. They cannot touch me.'

'But you spoke a Law.'

He laughed. 'Will you denounce me?' he asked.
'Will you have me burned?'

My crushed fingers throbbed. I was finding it hard to stand up
straight. I'd always thought the Thing knew nothing of the past,
but the Inquisitor was not ignorant. Far from it: he knew as much
as me, or more. I was afraid. What would it mean if he understood
what we had lost, and didn't care to save it?

The Inquisitor lifted his arms over his head in a cat-like stretch.

'I am here,' he said, simply. 'Unlike you, I am in this moment. Half of you is still back in the words I just spoke, in their twists and turns, the power you think they hold. But I'm here, on this peak. I can raise my hands to the sun, feel the wind on my face. Life is already revealed to my senses. Do you see the difference?'

I said nothing.

'You venerate our ancestors, but you don't understand them. Truth is, they castrated themselves. The only reason a man has to make a mark on a screen is because he lacks something. They broke open the world because they wanted to control its power. Why? Because they'd lost their own.'

'You know the words of Darwing.'

'They're just words. I'm trying to show you that you can't replace life with signs. They could never be enough.'

'But the penalty for speaking a Law is death.'

'I'm a special case.'

'Please, tell me. How do you know those words?'

He smiled. 'Now you are wondering if I'm a Lawlord. You want me to tell you how to build animals? Perhaps you'd like to see a working screen. Would you like to see that? A screen, spilling sign out into the air?'

My heart was in my mouth. I nodded.

He laughed at me, a big hearty laugh.

'You really have fallen far. I bring you up here, where
the air is clean, and this is all you want? I show you the
sunlight and you'd rather see flickering on a screen!
There's a cleft in the middle of your spirit, my friend.
A crack. The world is the world of the senses, nothing
more. Sight and sound and touch. The rest is illusion.'

'The ancestors could heal illnesses, they could fly. They had electricity.'

'The ancestors almost destroyed the world. You know, of
course, about the Magnetization. I expect that's the sort
of thing you talk about in your little secret meetings.'

It was a trap, but I didn't care. I'd condemned myself ten times already.
'They saw lights. In the heavens. An aura.'

'Very good. Another banned word. Those lights
were made of sign. The pure strength of the Mother.
The ancestors saw the aura sign and it scraped their
machines clean. It was a complete surprise; even
their deepest internets hadn't predicted it. The chaos
was unimaginable. Millions died. Their so-called
civilization collapsed at a stroke. Of course, some fools
wanted to build it up again, but the wiser ones knew
the Mother was correcting the balance, re-establishing
the natural order of things. The Lawlords had exalted
themselves too far. They'd tipped the world out of true.
Memory has a certain poetry, but some things are better
forgotten. That's what I understand and you don't.
There are some powers we weren't meant to wield.'

'But we have no power. We're like – like animals.'

'Oh my friend, you're so sad. Don't be sad. If only
you understood what is being done. We're bringing
about the time of no time, the year whose number
is no number, when all will be softness on the skin
and sweetness in the mouth. Forgetting is at the root
of it. If you follow the path of forgetting you'll have
freedom of heart and peace of mind. You will have
a clear conscience.'

Something about this speech broke me. The Inquisitor knew secrets
that he would not tell. He knew things I would die without knowing.
And still he didn't care. Of course he spotted it – the little collapse in
my spirit. It was what he'd been angling for. Despair is only possible
when you have hope. Adroitly, skilfully, he had offered me hope and
then snatched it away. By bringing me to that place he'd undermined
me more efficiently than all the hours of torture.

He was right. How could I have doubted it? Memory had planted
a hunger in me. I was starving; I would always crave more. To know
more, to remember more. To number the world higher and higher.
Nothing would ever be enough.

Tears began to stream down my cheeks. He murmured into my ear,
in the same insidious tone he had used when offering me water.

'Release yourself into the time of no time, the thought which
undoes all thought. You have too much pride. Be modest.
Live simply. Then you'll find yourself here, on this hill.
Then at last you will be happy.'

I nodded. I belonged to him.

He gave a sign. The hood was replaced. In the darkness, I was loaded
on to the cart and taken away. Back at the prison, I told him every
name I knew.

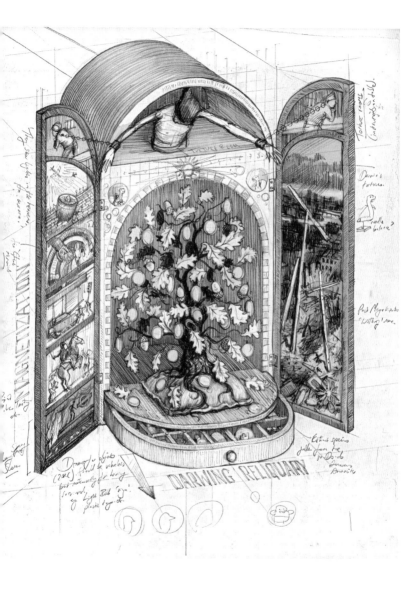

DARWIN RELIQUARY

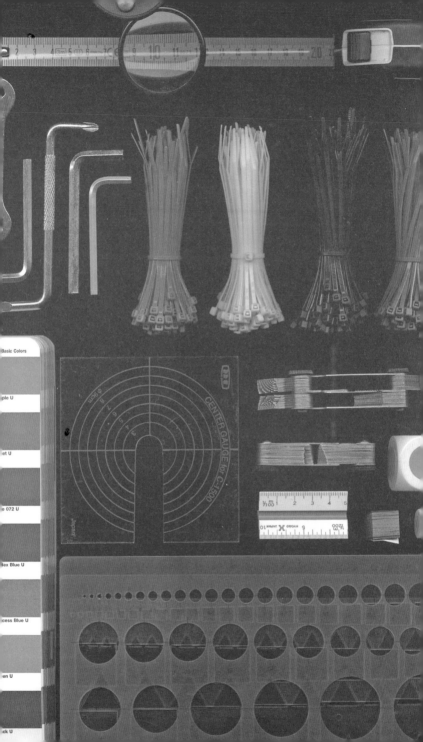

*

Now I'm no longer of any use, my guards show themselves to me.
They are ordinary, unremarkable men. One even speaks to me.
This morning he told me the day of my execution has been set.
He tried to prepare me. Think about the heartbeat, he said.
Quieten your mind and listen to the drum.

I can't quieten my mind. It is as if a thousand voices were hissing
at me at once. Every symbol in every niche of my memory palace
is spilling forth. A cacophony. A collapse.

On a deep crack in the wooden tabletop I put a spell or essay by a
minor Lawlord known as the Pope. It is an instruction to dominate
the world with number:

> Go wander creature where sign guides.
> Go measure earth, weigh air and state the tides
> Instruct the planets in what orbs to run
> Memorize old time and regulate the sun.

Now it seems to me that this is an injunction to sin. It is prideful,
overreaching. Tomorrow they will come for me. I will be taken to Soon
Square and my life will be over. Have I thrown it away for nothing?

In another crack on the table I have placed the Laws of Milord
Kelvin. They are the most awful of all Laws, and are called the Laws
of Endtropy, or just the Laws of the End. They are mysterious, and
many of the words are obscure, though they have been passed down
among us with great care. They appear to me as an eye, from which
fall three black tears.

1. There is at present in the material world a universal tendency to the dissipation of mechanical energy.

2. Any restoration of mechanical energy, without more than an equivalent of dissipation, is impossible in inanimate material processes, and is probably never effected by means of organized matter, either endowed with vegetable life or subject to the will of an animated creature.

3. Within a finite period of time past, the earth must have been, and within a finite period of time to come the earth must again be, unfit for the habitation of man as at present constituted, unless operations have been, or are to be performed, which are impossible under the laws to which the known operations going on at present in the material world are subject.

This is what I wonder. Is the Wilding just the earth making itself unfit for our habitation? Is it preparing to let us go?

*

I am curled up on the bed, thinking about the end, when I notice that I am covered in dust. Small chips of plaster are falling from the wall. I watch, in wonder, as a drill bit pokes through from the other side. Slowly the hole gets bigger, until it is about the size of an ancient coin.

I put my eye to it.

Another eye stares back at me.

'Put your ear against the hole and listen.'

It is a woman's voice, low and urgent. I do what she says.

>'We don't have much time. The fellowship have sent me.
>You must download.'

'But – I've betrayed you. You aren't safe. I told them everything.'

>'It doesn't matter.'

'I told them everything.'

>'And now you must tell me. I will receive all your
>memories. I will keep them safe. It's time for you
>to give up your burden. Load it down on me.'

'How did you get here?

>'None of that matters.
>We have friends, even in this place.'

'I'm going to die.'

>'Yes. I'm sorry. If we could get you out, we would, but
>it's beyond our powers. You're going to die and you'll
>be forgotten, unless you download on to me. You must
>do it. Nothing is more important.'

'But –'

>'All of it. Begin at the beginning. Work through
>everything. I will receive it. I will make sure it
>doesn't get lost.'

And this is what we do. I forget about forgetting. I put my mouth to the hole in the wall and speak. One by one I tell my memories. One by one the bright symbols of my memory palace are extinguished, like candles being snuffed out. I keep on speaking until I have recited all the things I was given to remember. She listens in silence, except when she asks me to repeat a difficult phrase. At the end, I am in darkness. Everything I have devoted myself to – everything I am – has flowed to the other side of the wall.

> 'Friend,' she says at last. 'You know about the last ritual of the download?'

'Yes.'

> 'Think carefully before you speak.'

This is what we do for the dying. I am permitted to add one memory of my own to the store. The others will hold it, will cherish it as carefully as the words of a Lawlord. After I am gone, it is all that will remain.

I think. This is what I choose to tell her.

> *I am walking over a green field, with my lover. In front of us scampers our cowardly little dog. My lover and I hold hands. I see her long dark hair, feel the cool pressure of her hand in mine. We walk over the field. Up ahead is the brow of a hill. In a moment, we will reach the top and be able to see the view.*

This is what I tell the listener at the hole in the wall.

This is what of mine will survive.

CURATING
A BOOK

*Laurie Britton Newell
and Ligaya Salazar*

In an age in which reading formats are rapidly changing, and print – as book, newspaper or magazine – is losing its dominance as a deliverer of the written word, it is appropriate to think about ideas of what 'reading' is – and what a book might be. Digital platforms enable us to engage with narrative in new ways, but when texts are searchable, layers of background information are immediately accessible at the touch of a fingertip, and dialogue with other readers is possible in real time, it is interesting to question what is happening to our experience of reading stories. How far can you push the format and still call something a book? *Memory Palace* is a physically immersive illustrated story that explores the idea of an exhibition as a walk-in book.

Digital publishing has not just changed the experience of readers, it has also altered the role of graphic designers and illustrators, who must now consider a more complex set of technological networks and possibilities as they work on-screen, where text rarely exists in isolation. The limits of how a designer might once have influenced the reading experience – font, letter and line spacing, paper stock, first cover impression – are no longer all-confining. As curator Andrew Blauvelt observed, 'in the future, most designers will be creating reading experiences not book designs'. [1]

While it would seem as if physical books might be losing importance, the physicality of an individual book is increasingly significant. Publishing houses experiment with material and printing techniques to create collectable cover designs and unusual formats. So if readers buy fewer 'real' books, it makes sense that those they do buy should be beautiful objects. This enables graphic designers and illustrators to work on book projects with more varied visual content and material qualities. The Dutch book designer Irma Boom, creator of some of the most highly acclaimed book designs published in recent years, observed in an interview: 'in older days, a book was made for spreading information, but now we have the Internet to spread information. So to spread something else – maybe sheer beauty or a much slower, more thought-provoking message – it's the book.' [2]

Set against this shifting context, *Memory Palace* provides an experiential reading format for a story. The exhibition brings together a new piece of fiction with 20 original commissions from graphic designers and illustrators to create an exhibition that can be *read*.

Unlike reading a printed book, visiting an exhibition is not usually a linear experience. A narrative that moved around in time and that could be accessed in different ways seemed like a good starting point for a story that would be encountered physically. The search for an author began with writers who had previously written non-linear narratives. We were drawn to Hari Kunzru because he had published novels and a book of short stories that play explicitly with sequence, time and disparate characters tied together by a central theme – a computer virus in his novel *Transmission*, and a rock formation in the Arizona desert in *Gods Without Men*. [3]

To experiment with the relationship between the written word and its visual interpretation fully, we commissioned a new story rather than attempt to adapt an existing text. This allowed the text to be created and finalized collaboratively, and meant that there would be no existing reader expectations – a narrative world that was untouched, ready to be populated with words and images. The original brief to Kunzru was very open, only setting out that multiple practitioners would be commissioned to interpret it, and that the outcome was to be an immersive narrative experience situated in a gallery in the Victoria and Albert Museum.

In response Kunzru created a dystopian story that mourns the loss of human knowledge. The central character is fascinated with the past and clings on to the few garbled memory fragments of it that still exist. The practice of 'Ars Memoria' or 'Mnemonics', a memory technique in which an imaginary building or environment is visualized and the information to be remembered is placed as 'objects' within the fictional space, bears comparison to the idea of a museum as a repository of past ideas. When Kunzru submitted the first draft of the text, it also became apparent that he had interwoven the collaborative basis of the project into the overarching themes of the story – that memories change in the mouths of those who tell them.

The text is written in passages that move between a sequence of interrogations and an 'unordered' series of memory fragments. We selected one or more passages to give to 20 different graphic designers and illustrators, who were able to respond to it freely. Each practitioner reacted to the words in the text very differently: some attempted to convey the complete passage, others stripped it back to one important event or sentence, and some even layered the narrative with words of their own. These commissions have gone beyond literal visualizations of the text and instead have added new meaning and direction to the story.

The chosen practitioners work across a variety of fields within graphics and illustration, from graphic novels and editorial illustration to advertising and typography. All have a background either in graphic design or illustration – disciplines that were traditionally tied to the world of books and print but which today span many different types of media and formats. While by no means intended as a survey show, the broad selection of contributors demonstrates the exceptionally diverse and expanding worlds of contemporary graphic design and illustration. What they share is a strong engagement with narrative, storytelling and words. The decisions to pair practitioners with passages of the text were based on both a strong visual resonance with their previous work and events in the story. An understanding of the physicality of the exhibition space and how the viewer might engage with their work was also a key aspect.

Four practitioners interpreted the passages of the story that set out the context and the world that the central character inhabits. Francesco Franchi and Stefanie Posavec, both of whom work in the field of information graphics and have a keen interest in making complex connections visible, interpreted the utopian 'Wilding' and how the art of memory is practised. The illustrator Mario Wagner, who works primarily with digital and collage techniques, captured

'Magnetization', the magnetic storm that wiped out all technology
in the world. The illustrator Frank Laws, who is concerned with
documenting intricate details of mundane reality, such as brickwork,
was tasked with depicting the prisoner's current setting, the cell.

The central passages of dialogue in the story, a series of interrogations
between the prisoner and his captor, were portrayed by the illustrators
Luke Pearson, Alexis Deacon and Jim Kay, who have backgrounds
in graphic novels and children's books. They document the prisoner's
ultimate confession and demise in a series of powerfully drawn
sequences that form the narrative spine of the story.

Interspersed around the interrogations are the memory fragments the
prisoner has been tasked to remember. Some of the misremembered
facts and playful definitions have been depicted by the typographers
Peter Bil'ak, Oded Ezer and Hansje van Halem, who have all worked
with Kunzru's words from the memory fragments, presenting them
in unusual formats: giant reversible letters, floor tiles and drawn
type shown on Skype. The graphic artist Sam Winston has taken
the prisoner's text as a starting point to write more text, which he
has incorporated into a sprawling, intricate periodic table.

The illustrator Henning Wagenbreth and the collective Le Gun,
who are interested in working off the page with different surfaces
and spaces, were given the memory passages about museums and
hospitals, which they have reimagined in three-dimensional drawn
environments. The graphic designer Erik Kessels has also taken
the passages of text about recycling and advertising into the physical
realm, creating a giant recycled paper palace. The 'Laws of Endtropy'
are visualized as a large advertising board conceived by the graphic
designer Na Kim and in another corrupted memory the laws of Newton
have been brought to life in the shape of an altarpiece created and
illustrated by Stuart Kolakovic.

To explore ideas about different viewpoints and interpretations,
two practitioners and a collective were asked to work on the passage

about the prisoner's past and his induction into the 'Memorialists'. The illustrator Isabel Greenberg, who creates graphic novels, sought to sequence the relationship between the prisoner and his teacher Billgee. The illustrator Némo Tral, who works on architectural drawings, chose to depict the ruins of iconic London buildings and the Olympic Park where the prisoner grew up. The graphic design collective Åbäke have evoked the apocalyptic setting of the story to question the meaning of a collection of objects when all knowledge about what function they serve is lost.

Johnny Kelly, who has a background in graphic design and animation, was asked to interpret the end of the story and created a physical and interactive installation that acts as a memory bank for visitors to add to, generating life for the story beyond the exhibition.

The exciting breadth of visual responses and number of people involved in the project also posed an unusual challenge: how to create an experience for the visitor that would be cohesive. It required a careful pacing of the story within the physical space, a narrative life raft for the visitor, and a strong overarching exhibition design. In an attempt to further integrate the sequence of the story and the design of the exhibition, several meetings were held at an early stage in the project between the curators, Hari Kunzru, the architect and exhibition designer C.J. Lim and the graphic designers of Sara De Bondt studio. As a result, the design of the exhibition draws on the underlying themes of the story itself and unifies the diverse elements of the project.

C.J. Lim created a large building to contain the story. Like a palace of memories, it is made up of a space that contains the narrative spine of the story and a series of individual chambers, each containing a different memory fragment. The layout of the exhibition gives visitors a choice about which direction to turn and which passage to encounter next. Each visitor's experience is slightly different depending on the route they choose to walk through the story, and all ultimately leave with their own version.

Sara De Bondt studio, who also designed this book, created the exhibition graphics that grow over the walls of the building like moss or ivy and reflect one of the central ideas in the story – nature overtaking the built landscape. The studio's choice of typeface used both here in the book and for the exhibition graphics is Jenson, based on Golden Type, which was designed by William Morris in 1890. The studio chose it because they saw a connection between the time of the 'Wilding' and Morris's vision of a pre-industrial Utopia.

Kunzru's complete text is not present in the exhibition itself; rather, a pared down version is displayed, giving the visitor a narrative thread to follow. In an attempt to let the story be told purely through the words of the author and visual responses of the practitioners, where the words and images tell different yet connected and supporting plots, there are no object labels or factual information inside the exhibition.

Memory Palace is at its core a collaboration between word and image. It is a narrative made up of multiple viewpoints that have come together to create a story that can be walked through, observed and read. Interpretation and translation underpin the entire project, from the central premise of the story itself to the ways in which each practitioner has responded, and ultimately the way in which the visitor engages with the narrative. *Memory Palace* explores what happens when a story leaves the pages of a book and enters the gallery space.

1   Andrew Blauvelt, 'From Books to Texts', in Mieke Gerritzen, Geert Lovink
     and Minke Kampman (eds), *Exploring New Information Cultures* (Breda 2011)
2   Erich Nagler, 'Irma Boom's Visual Testing Ground: The Internationally Acclaimed
     Book Designer Talks about her Craft', *Metropolis Magazine* (29 February 2008),
     http://www.metropolismag.com/story/20080229/booms-visual-testing-ground
3   Hari Kunzru, *Transmission* (London 2004) and *Gods Without Men* (London 2011)

MAKING
MEMORY
PALACE

Robert Hunter

The illustrator Robert Hunter followed the development of the
Memory Palace project and in response produced a wordless
graphic story. It visualizes a part actual, part imaginary journey
through the process of making this storytelling experiment.

Memory Palace
Hari Kunzru

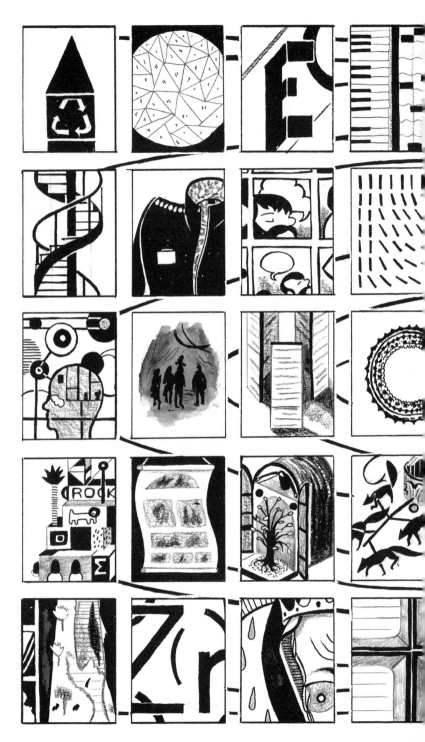

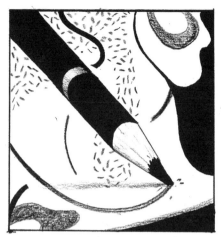

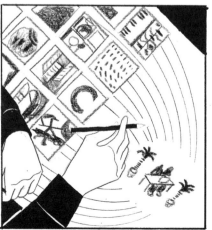

Åbäke is a collective of graphic designers formed in London in 2000 by Patrick Lacey, Kajsa Ståhl, Benjamin Reichen and Maki Suzuki. Much of their work concentrates on the social aspect of design and the strength that collaboration can bring to a project. abake.fr / dentdeleone.co.nz
→ pp.60 – 61

Peter Bil'ak is a graphic designer and typographer based in The Hague. He founded his design studio and type foundry Typotheque in 1999. He combines his own design practice with teaching, curating and writing about graphic design and typography. peterbilak.com
→ p.65

Laurie Britton Newell is the co-curator of *Memory Palace*. She has devised and curated projects for the V&A including *Make Lab* and *No Strings* in 2011, *1:1, Architects Build Small Spaces* in 2010 and *Out of the Ordinary: Spectacular Craft* in 2008.

Alexis Deacon is an award-winning writer and illustrator of children's books based in London. His books, illustrated predominantly by hand, are poignant and captivating journeys into imaginary worlds. alexisdeacon.co.uk
→ pp.38, 41, 49

Sara De Bondt studio works extensively with cultural clients creating exhibitions and publications with a strong emphasis on typographic detailing combined with subtle playfulness. saradebondt.com / occasionalpapers.org

Oded Ezer – often described as an 'experimental typographer' – is a graphic and type designer based in Tel Aviv. Ezer's work pushes the world of words into new realms. His typography has been collected by numerous international museums. ezerdesign.com
→ pp.36, 66

Francesco Franchi is a graphic designer and journalist based in Milan. Franchi's intricate infographics combine images, words and numbers to communicate complex ideas with great efficiency and beauty. francescofranchi.com
→ pp.10 – 11

Isabel Greenberg is a London-based illustrator and comic artist. Her touching and evocative graphic novels are created using a combination of hand drawing and digital techniques. isabelnecessary.com

→ P.56

Hansje van Halem works as an independent graphic designer in Amsterdam with a focus on book design and print. In much of her work she intricately and painstakingly draws letters and patterns in what she describes as 'an ode to patience'. hansje.net

→ P.27

Robert Hunter is a London-based illustrator who works with traditional drawing and printing techniques to produce his otherworldly picture narratives. rob-hunter.co.uk

Jim Kay is an award-winning illustrator of children's books based in Northamptonshire. He creates haunting and powerful scenes and characters by experimenting with different materials and techniques for each project. jimkay.co.uk

→ PP.68, 73

Johnny Kelly is a graphic designer from Ireland who works across animation, graphic design and illustration. His award-winning animations have been screened internationally and he has created a number of innovative cross-platform projects with Nexus Productions. mickeyandjohnny.com nexusproductions.com

→ PP. 78 – 79

Erik Kessels, the founder and creative director of the communications agency KesselsKramer based in Amsterdam, is a graphic designer, curator and photography collector. KesselsKramer's witty and irreverent work is often described as 'anti-advertising'. kesselskramer.com

→ PP.28 – 29

Na Kim is a graphic designer based in Seoul who is the editor and art director of *Graphic* magazine. She works predominantly with cultural and editorial clients, creating playful and colourful design and print. ynkim.com

→ P.74

Stuart Kolakovic is an illustrator based in Staffordshire. Working under the pseudonym Herman Inclusus he has created a body of work that references both medieval illuminated manuscripts and Eastern European traditions of religious iconography. stuartkolakovic.co.uk / hermaninclusus.co.uk

→ PP.20 – 21

Hari Kunzru is the author of four novels, including *The Impressionist*, published in 2002, and *Gods Without Men*, published in 2011. His work has won him prizes including the Somerset Maugham Award, the Betty Trask Prize awarded by the Society of Authors and a British Book Award. harikunzru.com

Frank Laws is a London-based illustrator with a fascination for capturing the mundane details of everyday life. He works in watercolour, ink and acrylic paint on paper, applying layer upon layer to obtain richness and depth. franklaws.com

→ PP.23 – 24

Le Gun is a London-based illustration collective founded by Neal Fox, Chris Bianchi, Bill Bragg, Robert Rubbish, Matthew Appleton, Alex Wright and Stephanie von Reiswitz. Their large-scale, communally executed witty drawings, murals and three-dimensional drawn installations have been exhibited internationally. legun.co.uk

→ PP.18 – 19

C.J. Lim is an architect and a professor at the Bartlett School for Architecture in London. He is the director of Studio 8 Architects. Lim creates intricate paper models that combine imaginative cityscapes with playful and poetic narratives. cjlim-studio8.com

Luke Pearson is a comic book artist and illustrator based in Nottingham. The subjects in his stories range from surreal folk tales to very human tales of estrangement and heartbreak. lukepearson.com

→ PP.31 – 32

Stefanie Posavec is an American graphic designer based in London who works with text and data. She is interested in using objective information as a medium to generate visuals and communicate subjective messages. itsbeenreal.co.uk

→ PP.13 – 14

Ligaya Salazar is the co-curator of *Memory Palace*. She devised and curated V&A contemporary projects including *Yohji Yamamoto* and *No Strings* in 2011, *British Fashion* in 2009, *Fashion V Sport* in 2008 and *Crafting Couture* in 2007.

Némo Tral is an illustrator based in Paris. He studied architecture and continues to work in this field, describing his interest in buildings as something he arrived at through drawing them. He creates ephemeral installations and graphic novels as stories to occupy forgotten urban spaces. nemotral.prosite.com

→ PP.51 – 53

Henning Wagenbreth is an independent illustrator and graphic designer based in Berlin. He uses techniques such as linocut, vector drawings, pen and ink, geometric shapes and distorted perspectives to make images more abstract yet easily legible. wagenbreth.com

→ PP.17, 48

Mario Wagner is a German illustrator based in San Francisco. He creates large-scale paper collage and photomontage works that bring together disparate elements from vintage magazines and pairs them with dark futuristic scenes and geometric marks in exciting juxtapositions. mario-wagner.com

→ P.43

Sam Winston is a graphic artist based in London. He creates sculpture, drawings and books that play with our understanding of language and words, both as carriers of messages and meaning and as visual information itself. samwinston.com

→ PP.46 – 47

First published by V&A Publishing, 2013
Victoria and Albert Museum
South Kensington
London SW7 2RL
www.vandapublishing.com

ISBN 978 1 85177 736 5

10 9 8 7 6 5 4 3 2
2015 2014 2013

A catalogue record for this book is available from the British Library.

Design: Sara De Bondt studio
Copy-editor: Howard Watson

Printed in China

V&A Publishing

Supporting the world's leading
museum of art and design,
the Victoria and Albert
Museum, London